P9-DFY-287

ALSO AVAILABLE FROM 🌳 JOE BOOKS

Disney Frozen Cinestory Comic

Disney Cinderella Cinestory Comic

Disney 101 Dalmatians Cinestory Comic

Disney Big Hero 6 Cinestory Comic

Disney•Pixar Inside Out Cinestory Comic

Disney Winnie the Pooh Cinestory Comic

Disney Princess Comics Treasury

Disney•Pixar Comics Treasury

Disney's Darkwing Duck: The Definitively
Dangerous Edition

Disney Phineas and Ferb Colossal Comics Collection

Disney Frozen: The Story of the Movie in Comics

Disney•Pixar Inside Out: The Story of
the Movie in Comics

Disney•Pixar Inside Out Fun Book

Published in the United States by Joe Books
Publisher: Adam Fortier
President: Steve Osgoode
COO: Jody Colero
CEO: Jay Firestone

567 Queen St W, Toronto, ON M5V 2B6 Canada
www.joebooks.com

ISBN 978-1-987955-23-1 (Joe Books edition, US)
First Joe Books Edition: JULY 2015
1 3 5 7 9 10 8 6 4 2

Copyright © 2015 Disney Enterprises, Inc. All rights reserved.

Published in the United States by Joe Books, Inc.

No portion of this publication may be reproduced or transmitted, in any form or by any means, without the express written permission of the copyright holders.

Names, characters, places, and incidents featured in this publication are either the product of the author's imagination or are used fictitiously. Any resemblance to actual persons (living or dead), events, institutions, or locales, without satiric intent, is coincidental.

Joe Books™ is a trademark of Joe Books, Inc. Joe Books® and the Joe Books Logo are trademarks of Joe Books, Inc., registered in various categories and countries. All rights reserved.

Printed in USA through Avenue4 Communications at Cenveo/Richmond, Virginia

For information regarding the CPSIA on this printed material, call: (203) 595-3636 and provide reference #RICH - 625247.

EDITOR AND DESIGNER Rob Tokar • SENIOR EDITOR Carolynn Prior
SENIOR EDITOR Robert Simpson • EXECUTIVE EDITOR Amy Weingartner
PRODUCTION COORDINATOR Stephanie Alouche

Thanks to David Gerstein for his impeccable research and invaluable assistance.

SPECIAL THANKS TO DISNEY PUBLISHING: Teri Avanian • Curt Baker • Julie Dorris
Behnoosh Khalili • Arianna Marchione • Manny Mederos • Beatrice Osman
Charlene Pugh and the rest of the Disney Publishing Worldwide Comics Team.

Contents

Contents

Contents

DISNEP's

THE LITTLE
MERMAID

EH?

I JUST DON'T *SEE* THINGS THE WAY DADDY DOES! A WORLD THAT MAKES SUCH WONDERFUL THINGS *CAN'T* BE BAD!

BUT IT ISN'T JUST *THINGS* I WANT! IT'S BEING WHERE THE *PEOPLE* LIVE!

I'D GIVE ANYTHING TO *LIVE* UP THERE, BREATHING THE AIR AND GOING ANYWHERE I *PLEASED!*

OOPS!

HOW I'D *LOVE* TO LIVE IN THAT WORLD SOMEDAY!

SEBASTIAN!

POP!

ARGH!

ARIEL, WHAT ARE YOU-- AH, HOW COULD YOU--EH-- WHAT *IS* ALL *DIS??*

JUST MY COLLECTION!

THE THIRD MORNING...

ARIEL! WAKE UP! CONGRATU-LATIONS!

WE *DID* IT, KIDDO!

THE WHOLE *TOWN'S* BUZZING ABOUT THE PRINCE GETTING HIMSELF *HITCHED* THIS AFTERNOON!

JUST WANNA WISH YOU *LUCK!* SEE YOU AT THE *WEDDING*-- I WOULDN'T *MISS* IT!

WHAT IS DIS IDIOT *BABBLING* ABOUT??

NOW, ERIC--ER--IT APPEARS I WAS *MISTAKEN!* THIS--UM--MYSTERY MAIDEN OF YOURS *DOES* IN FACT *EXIST!*

AND SHE IS *LOVELY!* CON-GRATU...

WE WISH TO BE MARRIED AS SOON AS *POSSIBLE!*

OF *COURSE*, ERIC, BUT THESE THINGS DO TAKE TIME, AND--

THIS *AFTER-NOON*, GRIMSBY!

THE WEDDING SHIP DEPARTS BEFORE SUNSET!

≡SIGH!≡ AS YOU *WISH*, ERIC!

I believe in
discovering the beauty
in the world around me
and finding the power
of my own voice.

I am a Princess

Ariel

"AHHH-- SALAAM AND GOOD EVENING TO YOU, WORTHY FRIEND!"

"PLEASE, PLEASE, COME CLOSER..!"

KJN007/D92222

WELCOME TO AGRABAH! CITY OF MYSTERY... ...OF ENCHANTMENT...

...OF THE FINEST MERCHANDISE THIS SIDE OF THE RIVER JORDAN! PERHAPS A BEAUTIFUL ANTIQUE POT...

PERHAPS YOU WOULD BE MOST REWARDED TO CONSIDER--

--THIS!

DO NOT BE FOOLED BY ITS COMMONPLACE APPEARANCE! LIKE SO MANY THINGS, IT IS NOT WHAT IS OUTSIDE, BUT WHAT IS INSIDE, THAT COUNTS!

THIS LAMP ONCE CHANGED THE COURSE OF A YOUNG MAN'S LIFE--A YOUNG MAN WHO HIMSELF WAS NOT QUITE WHAT HE SEEMED...

PERHAPS YOU WOULD LIKE TO HEAR THE TALE?

"IT BEGINS ON A DARK NIGHT...

"...WHERE A DARK MAN WAITS...

"...WITH A DARK PURPOSE..."

YOU ARE LATE.

NOW REMEMBER-- BRING ME THE LAMP! THE REST OF THE TREASURE IS YOURS, BUT THE LAMP IS MINE!

NOW GO!

WHO DISTURBS MY SLUMBER?

IT IS... IT IS... I... GAZEEM... A HUMBLE THIEF!

KNOW THIS-- ONLY ONE MAY ENTER HERE!

ONE WHOSE WORTH LIES FAR WITHIN!

THE DIAMOND IN THE ROUGH!

ROARRR!

AAAA-

CHOMMMMMPPP!

I CAN'T BELIEVE IT! WE'RE NEVER GONNA GET AHOLD OF THAT STUPID LAMP!

PATIENCE, IAGO. GAZEEM WAS OBVIOUSLY LESS THAN WORTHY.

WE MUST FIND THIS DIAMOND IN THE ROUGH...

ANOTHER DAY IN AGRABAH. THE START OF NEW AND GLORIOUS ADVENTURES FOR SOME...

...AND MORE OF THE SAME OLD PROBLEMS FOR OTHERS...

STOP, THIEF!! I'LL HAVE YOUR HANDS FOR A TROPHY, STREET RAT!

ALL THIS FOR A LOAF OF BREAD?!

OUT OF MY WAY, YOU WORTHLESS, FLEA-BITTEN *STREET RAT!*

HEY!!

I'M NOT *WORTHLESS!* I'M *NOT A STREET RAT!*

AND I *DON'T HAVE FLEAS!!*

THAT NIGHT...

WELL, HERE WE ARE—*HOME,* SWEET *HOME!*

SOMEDAY ALL THIS IS GONNA *CHANGE,* ABU. WE'LL BE DRESSED IN *ROBES* INSTEAD OF *RAGS,* AND BE *INSIDE* A PALACE LOOKING *OUT*...

...INSTEAD OF *OUTSIDE* LOOKING *IN.*

THAT'D BE THE LIFE, HUH? TO BE *RICH,* LIVE IN A *PALACE*...

...AND NEVER HAVE *ANY* PROBLEMS AT *ALL*...

—ATER, AT THE PALACE...

GAAH!! I'VE NEVER BEEN SO *INSULTED!*

PRINCE ACHMED—YOU'RE LEAVING SO *SOON?*

GOOD LUCK MARRYING *HER* OFF!

OH, *DEAR*...

HERE, JAFAR... WHATEVER YOU... NEED...WILL BE FINE...

YOU ARE MOST GRACIOUS, MY LIEGE. NOW, RUN ALONG AND PLAY, HMM?

YES... YES...

BUT ONCE JAFAR AND IAGO ARE ALONE...

PFUI! BLEECH! I CAN'T *STAND* IT ANY MORE! IF I GOTTA CHOKE DOWN ONE MORE OF THOSE MOLDY CRACKERS, I'LL--I'LL--

--I'LL GRAB HIM AROUND THE HEAD...WHAP! WHAP! WHAP! WHAP!

GLICK!

CALM YOURSELF, IAGO! *THIS* DIAMOND WILL *REVEAL* TO US THE *DIAMOND IN THE ROUGH*--

--THE ONE WHO CAN ENTER THE *CAVE* AND BRING US THE *LAMP!*

SOON I WILL BE SULTAN!

YEAH, AND THEN I STUFF THE CRACKERS DOWN *HIS* THROAT!

RRMMMBLLL

MEANWHILE, IN THE PALACE GARDENS...

I'M SORRY, RAJAH, BUT I *CAN'T* STAY HERE AND HAVE MY LIFE LIVED FOR ME.

I'LL MISS YOU...

GOOD-BYE!

PRRRR?

AND SOON, THE WONDERS OF THE MARKET-PLACE UNFOLD!

SUGARED DATES AND FIGS HERE!

FRESH FISH!

PRETTY LADY, BUY A *POT!* NO FINER POTS IN *BRASS* OR *SILVER!*

TRAGIC, ISN'T IT? BUT NO HARM DONE!

C'MON, SIS-- TIME TO GO SEE THE DOCTOR!

WHY, HELLO, DOCTOR!

HEY-- *PUT THOSE BACK!*

RUN! EEEK!

COME BACK HERE, YOU LITTLE THIEVES!

LATER, IN JAFAR'S SECRET LAB...

WITH ALL DUE *RESPECT*, YOUR ROTTENNESS ≡PANT PANT!≡ COULDN'T WE JUST WAIT FOR A ≡PANT PANT!≡ *REAL STORM?!*

SAVE YOUR BREATH, IAGO. FASTER!

YES, O MIGHTY EVIL ONE!

PART, SANDS OF TIME! REVEAL TO ME THE ONE WHO CAN *ENTER* THE CAVE!

YES...YES! THERE HE IS--

--MY *DIAMOND* IN THE *ROUGH!*

I'LL HAVE THE GUARDS EXTEND HIM AN *INVITATION* TO THE PALACE...

THAT EVENING...

THIS IS WHERE YOU LIVE?

YEP, JUST ME AND ABU. WE COME AND GO AS WE PLEASE. IT'S NOT MUCH, REALLY--

--BUT IT'S GOT A GREAT VIEW! THE PALACE LOOKS PRETTY AMAZING, HUH?

OH, YES... WONDERFUL....

I WONDER WHAT IT WOULD BE LIKE TO LIVE THERE... TO HAVE SERVANTS AND VALETS...

SURE. PEOPLE WHO TELL YOU WHERE TO GO AND HOW TO DRESS...

THAT'S BETTER THAN HERE! YOU'RE ALWAYS SCRAPING FOR FOOD AND DUCKING THE GUARDS...

YOU'RE NOT FREE TO MAKE YOUR OWN CHOICES.... WHAT TO DO, WHO TO MARRY...

SOMETIMES YOU FEEL SO--

YOU'RE JUST SO--

--TRAPPED!

HERE YOU ARE!

SO HOW'D IT GO?

I THINK SHE TOOK IT RATHER *WELL!*

AND OUTSIDE...

OH, RAJAH, =SOB= THIS IS ALL *MY* FAULT!

I DIDN'T EVEN KNOW HIS NAME...

LATER THAT NIGHT, AND NOT SO FAR AWAY...

YOU'RE ONLY A FOOL IF YOU *GIVE UP,* BOY!

WHO ARE YOU?

A LOWLY *PRISONER,* LIKE *YOURSELF,* BUT *TOGETHER,* PERHAPS WE CAN BE SOMETHING *MORE!*

SHE WAS THE *PRINCESS!* I CAN'T *BELIEVE* IT, ABU! I MUST'VE SOUNDED SO *STUPID* TO HER!

SHE'S GONNA MARRY A *PRINCE...* AND *I'M* A *FOOL...*

THERE IS A *CAVE,* BOY, FILLED WITH *TREASURES* BEYOND YOUR *WILDEST* DREAMS! TREASURE ENOUGH TO IMPRESS EVEN YOUR *PRINCESS,* I'D WAGER...

JAFAR, HURRY UP! I'M *DYIN'* IN HERE!

Shh!

SO WHY WOULD YOU SHARE ALL THIS TREASURE WITH *ME?*

I NEED A YOUNG PAIR OF *LEGS* AND A STRONG *BACK* TO GO IN AFTER IT!

Disney PRINCESS COMICS COLLECTION

AT LEAST *SOME* GOOD WILL COME OF MY BEING FORCED TO MARRY.

WHEN I AM *QUEEN*, I WILL HAVE THE POWER TO GET *RID* OF *YOU!*

HEH, HEH-HEH.

THERE, NOW. *THAT'S* SETTLED! NOW, *JASMINE...*

IF ONLY I'D GOTTEN THAT *LAMP!*

TO THINK WE GOTTA KEEP *KISSIN'* UP TO THAT *CHUMP* AN' HIS *CHUMP* DAUGHTER THE REST OF OUR LIVES!

NO, IAGO--ONLY UNTIL SHE FINDS A *CHUMP* HUSBAND! THEN SHE'LL HAVE US *BANISHED*, OR WORSE--

--BE-HEADED!

WAIT A MINUTE! WHAT IF *YOU* WERE THE CHUMP HUSBAND?!

YOU MARRY THE PRINCESS, *RIGHT?* THEN YOU BECOME *SULTAN!*

HMMM...

THE IDEA HAS MERIT...

MEAN-WHILE...

THANK YOU FOR CHOOSING MAGIC CARPET FOR ALL YOUR TRAVEL *NEEDS!* DON'T STAND UNTIL THE RUG HAS COME TO A COMPLETE *STOP!*

WELL, HOW 'BOUT *THAT*, MISTER DOUBTING MUSTAPHA?

EEEEK!

WHAT BETTER WAY TO MAKE YOUR *GRAND ENTRANCE* DOWN THE *STREETS* OF *AGRABAH* THAN RIDING YOUR *VERY OWN--*

POOF!

--*ESALUMBO SIIMBIM DUMBO!!*

TALK ABOUT YOUR *TRUNK SPACE!*

HE'S GOT THE *OUTFIT!* HE'S GOT THE *ELEPHANT!* BUT WE'RE NOT *THROUGH* YET!

HANG ONTO YOUR *TURBAN*, KID-- WE'RE GONNA MAKE YOU A *STAR!*

That AFTER-NOON, AT THE PALACE...

SIRE! I HAVE FOUND A *SOLUTION* TO THE PROBLEM WITH YOUR *DAUGHTER!*

RIGHT *HERE!*

"IF A PRINCESS HAS NOT CHOSEN A HUSBAND BY THE APPOINTED TIME, THEN THE *SULTAN* SHALL CHOOSE *FOR* HER!"

BUT JASMINE *HATED* ALL THOSE SUITORS! HOW CAN I *CHOOSE* SOMEONE SHE *HATES?*

NOT TO *WORRY*, MY LIEGE! THERE IS *MORE!*

"IF, IN THE EVENT A *SUITABLE* PRINCE *CANNOT BE FOUND*, A PRINCESS MAY BE WED TO...."

HMM...INTERESTING...THE *ROYAL VIZIER!* WHY, THAT WOULD BE--

--*ME!*

BUT I THOUGHT THE *LAW* SAYS THAT ONLY A *PRINCE* CAN MARRY A *PRINCESS!* I'M QUITE *SURE*--

AND THESE ARE *DESPERATE TIMES*, AREN'T THEY?

YOU WILL *ORDER* THE PRINCESS TO *MARRY* ME!

DESPERATE *TIMES* CALL FOR DESPERATE *MEASURES*, MY LORD!

I WILL....I WILL ORDER THE...THE...

WHA--? *WHAT?!* I *HEARD* SOMETHING!

MAKE WAY! MAKE WAY!

MAKE WAY FOR PRINCE ALI!!

IT'S THE FABULOUS PRINCE ALI! ABABWA! EVERYONE-- COME AND SEE!

LOOK AT ALL HIS CAMELS!

AND HORSES!

AND SERVANTS!

AND DANCING GIRLS!

THIS IS A VERY IMPRESSIVE YOUTH, JAFAR! IF WE'RE LUCKY, YOU WON'T HAVE TO MARRY JASMINE AFTER ALL!

I DON'T TRUST HIM, SIRE!

YOUR MAJESTY, I AM PRINCE ALI ABABWA! I HAVE JOURNEYED FROM AFAR TO SEEK YOUR DAUGHTER'S HAND!

THIS PRINCE ABOOBOO IS NO DIFFERENT THAN THE OTHERS! WHAT MAKES HIM THINK HE IS WORTHY OF THE PRINCESS?

JUST LET HER MEET ME, YOUR MAJESTY! I WILL WIN YOUR DAUGHTER!

HOW DARE YOU! ALL OF YOU! STANDING AROUND DECIDING MY FUTURE!

I AM NOT A PRIZE TO BE WON!

ER...DON'T WORRY, PRINCE ALI! JUST GIVE JASMINE TIME TO COOL DOWN! I'M SURE SHE'LL WARM TO YOU!

I THINK IT'S TIME TO SAY GOODBYE TO PRINCE ABOOBOO...

THAT NIGHT...

AL, TAKE SOME ADVICE-- IF YOU WANT TO COURT THE LITTLE LADY, BE YOURSELF!

WHAT--A STREET RAT? HEY, THAT'S THE LAST THING I WANT TO BE!

WHAT AM I GOING TO DO? JASMINE WON'T EVEN LET ME TALK TO HER!

I SHOULD HAVE KNOWN I COULDN'T PULL OFF THIS STUPID PRINCE WISH. GENIE, I NEED HELP!

I'M GOING TO GO SEE HER. I'VE GOT TO BE SMOOTH! COOL! CONFIDENT!

HOW DO I LOOK?

LIKE A PRINCE.

AND SO, FROM THE BALCONY...

PRINCESS JASMINE? IT'S ME-- PRINCE ALI!!

I DO NOT WANT TO SEE YOU!

PLEASE, PRINCESS-- GIVE ME A CHANCE!

GRRRR!

WAIT--DO I KNOW YOU?

UH--NO!

YOU REMIND ME OF SOMEONE I SAW IN THE MARKETPLACE...

THE MARKETPLACE? HA-HA! I, UH, I HAVE SERVANTS WHO GO TO THE MARKETPLACE FOR ME! WHY, I HAVE SERVANTS WHO GO FOR MY SERVANTS! SO IT COULDN'T HAVE BEEN ME YOU MET...

WELL, YOU KNOW...*ROYALTY* GOING OUT INTO THE CITY IN *DISGUISE*...IT SOUNDS A LITTLE *STRANGE*, DON'T YOU THINK?

NOT *THAT* STRANGE...

ONCE BACK AT THE PALACE...

GOOD NIGHT, MY HANDSOME PRINCE.

BUMP!

SLEEP WELL, PRIN-CESS.

≡SIGH!≡ FOR THE *FIRST TIME* IN MY *LIFE*, THINGS ARE STARTING TO GO *RIGHT!*

HUH--?!?

Aladdin

THIS IS *NOT DONE YET,* BOY!

FOOF!

GUARDS! ARREST JAFAR AT ONCE!

FIND HIM! SEARCH EVERY-WHERE...

I CAN'T *BELIEVE* IT! JAFAR---MY MOST *TRUSTED COUNSELLOR*... A *TRAITOR!* THIS IS *HORRIBLE,* JUST HOR--

CAN THIS BE *TRUE?* MY DAUGHTER HAS *FINALLY* CHOSEN A *SUITOR?!*

OH, YOU *BRILLIANT* BOY! YOU TWO WILL BE WED AT *ONCE,* AND SOMEDAY YOU WILL BE *SULTAN!*

SULTAN?!

SULTAN...?

MOMENTS LATER...

WE GOTTA GET *OUTTA* HERE, JAFAR! WE GOTTA START *PACKIN'!*

HEE-HEE-HEEE, HA *HA!!*

BOY, YEAH... HE'S *CRACKIN'* UP ON ME! JAFAR, GET A *GRIP!*

≡URK!≡ GOOD *GRIP!*

PRINCE ALI IS NOTHING MORE THAN THAT *RAGGED URCHIN ALADDIN!* HE HAS THE *LAMP,* IAGO!

AND *YOU* ARE GOING TO *RELIEVE* HIM OF IT!

NOW LISTEN *CLOSELY...*

Aladdin

Disney PRINCESS COMICS COLLECTION

SNOW. WIND. DESOLA-TION.

THE *ENDS* OF THE *EARTH*...

ABU?

ABU?!

ABU, ARE YOU OKAY?

I'M SORRY. I'VE MADE A MESS OF *EVERYTHING.* I SHOULD HAVE *FREED* THE GENIE WHEN I HAD THE CHANCE.

I'VE GOT TO GO BACK AND SET THINGS *RIGHT!* SOMEHOW...

CARPET! YOU'RE *HERE!*

EEEK!!

ALL RIGHT! BACK TO AGRABAH, LET'S *GO!*

LATER, IN THE PALACE HIGH ATOP THE MOUNTAIN...

IT *PAINS* ME TO SEE YOU *REDUCED* TO THIS, JASMINE.

A BEAUTIFUL DESERT BLOOM SUCH AS *YOURSELF* SHOULD BE ON THE ARM OF THE MOST *POWERFUL* MAN IN THE *WORLD!*

THEREFORE, I HAVE DECIDED TO MAKE MY *FINAL* WISH!

GENIE, I WISH FOR *PRINCESS JASMINE* TO FALL *DESPERATELY* IN *LOVE* WITH ME!

Disney PRINCESS COMICS COLLECTION

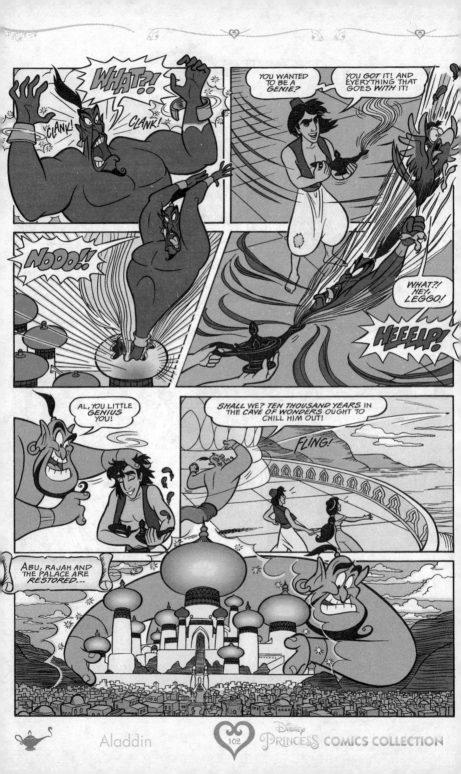

When I believe in
myself and take a chance
a whole new world awaits.

I am a Princess

Jasmine

Disney's

THE LITTLE MERMAID

"SERPENT TEEN"

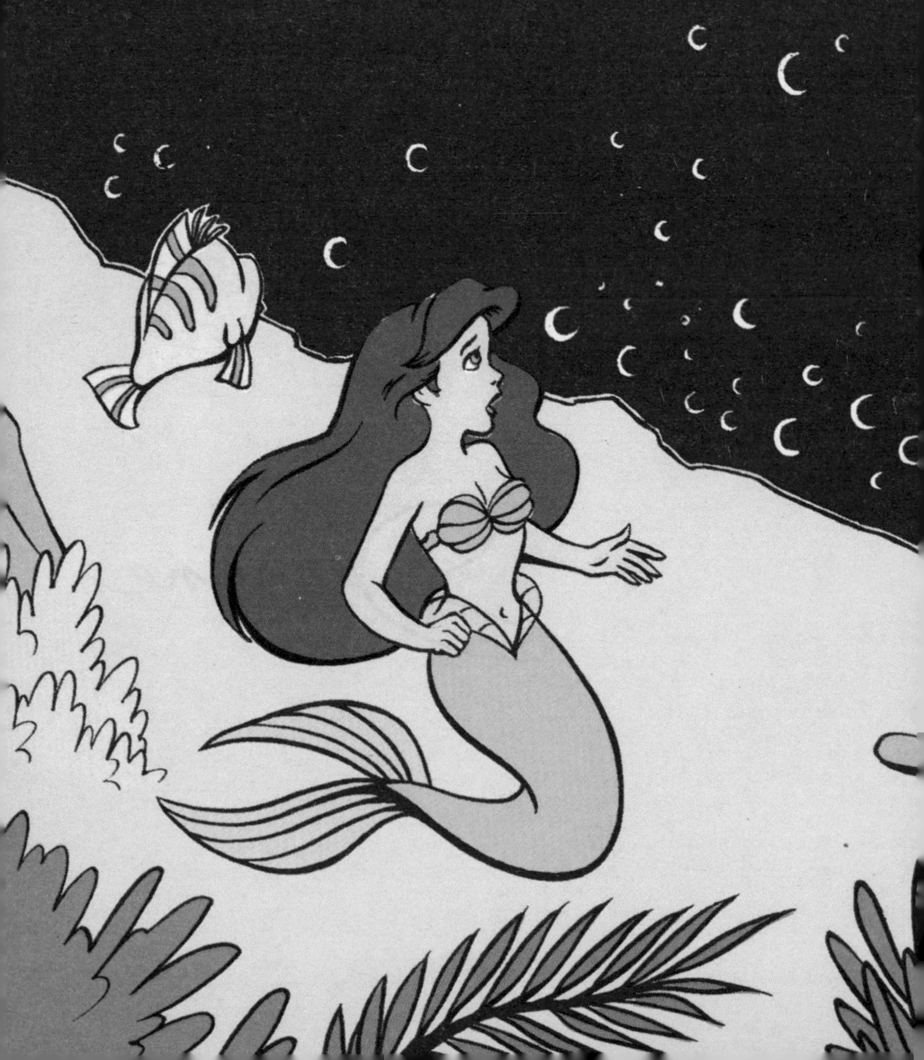

BUT THERE WERE MANY YEARS OF HOPING, DREAMING AND ADVENTURING BEFORE HER LIFE ON LAND BEGAN, YEARS SUCH AS THIS ONE -- WHEN SHE HAD JUST TURNED FIFTEEN --

AND A LIFE ABOVE THE WAVES WAS A MERE FANTASY, AS MUCH OF A FANTASY TO THE GIRL, WHO LIVED ON THE OCEAN FLOOR, AS HER OWN EXISTENCE WOULD BE TO THOSE WHO LIVED ON PARQUET FLOORS.

FOR, WHEN ALL WAS SAID AND DONE, THEY WERE STILL THE FORBIDDEN HUMANS. AND SHE, OF COURSE, WAS...

DISNEY'S

THE LITTLE MERMAID

FLOUNDER, YOU CAN BE SUCH A GUPPY.

I'M *NOT* A GUPPY.

THEN DON'T ACT LIKE ONE. "MELTING EYEBALLS," HONESTLY!

WELL, *THAT'S* WHAT--

YOU HEARD, I KNOW.

BUT I'M *TIRED* OF JUST HEARING THINGS. I WANT TO *SEE* THEM. EXPERIENCE THEM FIRST-HAND!

CAN'T YOU EXPERIENCE THEM FIRST-HAND BY LISTENING TO STORIES ABOUT THEM?

IT DOESN'T *WORK* THAT WAY, FLOUNDER.

WHAT *ARE* THEY?

THIS IS THE THIRD HUNTING TRIP THIS TIDE. HOW MANY MORE ARE WE SUPPOSED TO DO, ANYWAY?

AS MANY AS IT *TAKES* TO GET READY FOR THE FESTIVAL. THE SERPENTINE NEEDS TO BE KEPT FED UNTIL THE CELEBRATION BEGINS, UNLESS YOU WANT IT ANGRY AT YOU.

BESIDES, THE MOST INTERESTING CREATURES GET SENT DIRECTLY TO THE COLLECTION OF THE PRINCESS, AND SHE'S BEEN VERY DEMANDING LATELY. SHE WANTS NEW PETS.

HUNH! BETWEEN AN ANGRY PRINCESS AND AN ANGRY SERPENTINE, I'D TAKE MY CHANCES WITH THE *SERPENTINE*.

MY THOUGHTS EXACTLY.

COME ON, MOVE YOUR TAILS!

I GOTTA GET HELP!

BUT IF I TELL ANY OF THE GROWN-UPS BACK AT MERMAID CITY, THEN SOONER OR LATER, ARIEL'S DAD WILL FIND OUT!

WE'LL GET IN EVEN BIGGER TROUBLE THAN WE ARE RIGHT NOW!

I MEAN, WE WENT PAST THE BORDER! WE BROKE THE LAW! WHO KNOWS WHAT COULD HAPPEN IF KING TRITON FINDS OUT?!

BUT I GOTTA TALK TO A GROWN-UP TO FIGURE OUT WHAT TO DO!

I GOTTA!

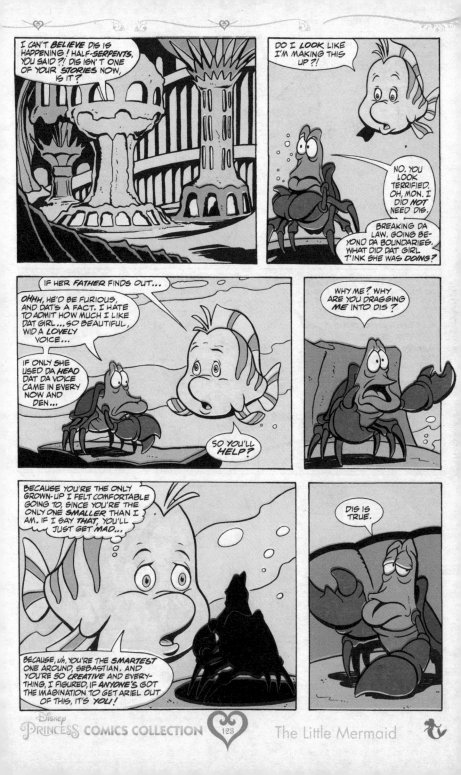

I CAN'T *BELIEVE* DIS IS HAPPENING! HALF-*SERPENTS*, YOU SAID?! DIS ISN'T ONE OF YOUR *STORIES* NOW, IS IT?

DO I *LOOK* LIKE I'M MAKING THIS UP?!

NO. YOU *LOOK* TERRIFIED. OH, MON. I DID *NOT* NEED DIS.

BREAKING DA LAW. GOING BE-YOND DA BOUNDARIES. WHAT DID DAT GIRL T'INK SHE WAS *DOING?*

IF HER *FATHER* FINDS OUT...

OHHH, HE'D BE FURIOUS, AND DAT'S A FACT. I HATE TO ADMIT HOW MUCH I LIKE DAT GIRL... SO BEAUTIFUL, WID A *LOVELY* VOICE...

IF ONLY SHE USED DA *HEAD* DAT DA VOICE CAME IN EVERY NOW AN DEN...

SO YOU'LL *HELP?*

WHY *ME?* WHY ARE YOU DRAGGING *ME* INTO DIS?

BECAUSE YOU'RE THE ONLY GROWN-UP I FELT COMFORTABLE GOING TO, SINCE YOU'RE THE ONLY ONE *SMALLER* THAN I AM. IF I SAY *THAT*, YOU'LL JUST GET MAD...

BECAUSE, uh, YOU'RE THE *SMARTEST* ONE AROUND, SEBASTIAN, AND YOU'RE SO *CREATIVE* AND EVERY-THING, I FIGURED, IF *ANYONE'S* GOT THE IMAGINATION TO GET ARIEL OUT OF THIS, IT'S *YOU!*

DIS IS TRUE.

NOW *THAT'S* ODD. I CAN'T RECALL EVER SEEING SEBASTIAN AND FLOUNDER HANGING ABOUT WITH EACH OTHER...

YET THERE THEY ARE...AND GOING SOMEPLACE IN AN AWFUL *HURRY.*

I'LL BET IT HAS SOMETHING TO DO WITH ARIEL. THAT'S THE ONLY THING THAT COULD GET FLOUNDER MOVING THAT QUICKLY.

THEN AGAIN, WHAT IF I'M *WRONG?* AM I SUPPOSED TO ASSIGN MEN TO FOLLOW THEM, AND IT TURNS OUT TO BE NOTHING? AND THEY'LL SAY, "THERE'S AQUATA AGAIN, PANICKING AS ALWAYS. SOME RULER-IN-TRAINING SHE IS."

AND THAT'S EXACTLY WHAT I'M DOING. BESIDES, WHATEVER ARIEL'S GOTTEN HERSELF MIXED UP IN...

FATHER WOULDN'T FEEL THE NEED TO GET HELP. HE'D SEE WHAT WAS GOING ON *PERSONALLY.*

"I'M SURE *I* CAN GET HER OUT OF IT."

LET ME *OUT* OF HERE.

YOU *SEE,* FATHER? I TOLD YOU SHE COULD SPEAK.

INCREDIBLE. JUST INCREDIBLE.

WHO COULD HAVE THOUGHT IT POSSIBLE? A CREATURE OF MYTH, RIGHT IN *FRONT* OF US.

YOU CAN UNDERSTAND WHAT I'M SAYING?

OF *COURSE* I CAN!

ALL RIGHT. THESE ARE MY PARENTS, THE KING AND QUEEN--*CORNELIUS* AND *AEMELIA*. MY NAME IS *CELIA*. I'M THE PRINCESS HERE, AND YOUR NEW OWNER.

NOBODY'S MY "OWNER." I'M *ARIEL*, I BELONG TO *MYSELF*, AND YOU HAVE NO BUSINESS KEEPING ME PRISONER HERE.

AND WHERE DO YOU COME FROM, ARIEL-WHO-BELONGS-TO-HERSELF?

FROM BEYOND THAT BIG CHASM WITH THE DARK WATER.

YOU'RE *LYING!* BEYOND THE CHASM IS JUST NOTHINGNESS! EVERY MORAY CHILD KNOWS THAT. THERE'S NO LIFE BEYOND THERE! IT'S DEATH TO EVEN TRY AND GO THERE!

MORAY? WHAT'S A *MORAY*?

WE ARE THE MORAY. AND MY DAUGHTER IS RIGHT. EVERY CHILD KNOWS THERE'S NO LIFE BEYOND THERE...

AND YET, WE CAN'T DENY THAT HERE YOU *ARE*. WHICH MEANS THAT THERE MAY INDEED BE MORE TO THE LEGENDARY HORROR STORIES OF HALF-FISH PEOPLE THAN WE CREDITED.

HORROR STORIES--?

OH, YES. SAVAGE, FREAKISH CREATURES THAT MAKE YOUR EYEBALLS MELT AND YOUR BRAIN FREEZE OVER AND YOUR *TONGUE* FALL OUT. MERE STORIES-- BUT THEN AGAIN, MAYBE NOT.

SO HOW MANY *MORE* OF YOU ARE THERE?

IF I TELL THEM ABOUT MY FAMILY...ABOUT MERMAID CITY...WHO KNOWS WHAT THEY'LL DO?

WE'RE NOT EXPECTING ANY KIND OF INVASION. WE'D GET *SLAUGHTERED!*

I HATE TO LIE, BUT I'VE GOT TO PROTECT MY PEOPLE.

ACTUALLY... I'M THE ONLY ONE OF MY KIND.

I WAS BORN IN THE SEA. MY MOTHER WAS A *DOLPHIN*. SHE DIED WHEN I WAS VERY YOUNG, AND NEVER TOLD ME ABOUT WHERE I CAME FROM. I NEVER KNEW *WHO* MY FATHER WAS.

YOU MIGHT SAY MY BIRTH WAS...

...SOMETHING OF A *FLUKE*.

THIS IS THE SERPENTINE CELEBRATION, ARIEL. ONE OF OUR MOST *POPULAR* EVENTS...

...IT CELEBRATES THE STRENGTH AND SKILL OF OUR HUNTERS AND WARRIORS. THEY NEED SOMETHING TO KEEP THEMSELVES SHARP... ESPECIALLY SINCE WE HAVE NO *ENEMIES* TO FIGHT.

OF COURSE, THAT WOULD *CHANGE* IF THERE WERE ANOTHER UNDERSEA RACE TO CONQUER. A PITY YOU'RE ONE OF A KIND.

I HOPE THOSE WEIGHTS AREN'T TOO UNCOMFORTABLE. BUT WE COULDN'T TAKE THE CHANCE OF YOU JUST SWIMMING OFF, COULD WE?

OH, *CERTAINLY NOT.*

WHAT HAPPENS IS, WE RELEASE OUR BEST HUNTERS INTO THE SERPENTINE MAZE WITH JUST SIMPLE KNIVES, AND THEY HAVE TO HUNT DOWN AND KILL A VERY SPECIAL TYPE OF BEAST THAT WE CAPTURED JUST FOR THE OCCASION, BEFORE THE BEAST KILLS *THEM*, OF COURSE.

SOUNDS CHARMING.

DOESN'T IT, THOUGH? AND WE HAVE SENTINELS WHO KEEP THE NET *HEAVILY* ELECTRIFIED SO THAT NO ONE CAN ESCAPE.

THIS YEAR, HOWEVER, SOMETHING HAS JUST COME UP. SO BEFORE WE RELEASE THE HUNTERS, WE'VE DECIDED TO GIVE THE BEAST A BIT OF A *SNACK*.

AH. *THERE'S* THE SNACK NOW.

YOU TOLD ME, ARIEL, THAT YOU WERE ONE OF A KIND. YET LOOK WHAT *WE* CAUGHT. AND I SUSPECT NOW THAT THERE'S A GREAT DEAL *MORE* OF YOU.

"*MOTHER WAS A DOLPHIN,*" INDEED. YOU SHOULD CHOOSE YOUR LIES MORE CAREFULLY.

NOW, I DON'T NEED *BOTH* OF YOU. WHAT I DO NEED IS INFORMATION. AND YOU'RE GOING TO GIVE IT TO ME, ARIEL. YOU'RE GOING TO TELL ME PRECISELY WHERE YOU COME FROM, AND EVERYTHING ABOUT YOUR PEOPLE THERE IS TO KNOW...

"...OR OTHERWISE YOUR FRIEND DOWN THERE IS GOING TO BE FISH FOOD.

NEXT: **SERPENT TEEN**

YOU **HEARD** ME, JUST **DON'T**.

DON'T FLOAT THERE WITH THAT **SMUG** EXPRESSION AND THINK THAT YOU'VE GOTTEN AWAY WITH SOMETHING. WE'LL GET YOUR "AQUATA" BACK.

NO, YOU **WON'T**. SHE'S THE FASTEST SWIMMER I KNOW, AND SHE WON'T BE TAKEN BY SURPRISE AGAIN!

CORNELIUS... CELIA... THIS IS ALL GOING **MUCH** TOO FAR. WE DON'T HAVE THE RIGHT TO--

OH, **DO** BE QUIET, MOTHER, NO ONE **ASKED** YOU.

DON'T YOU **TALK** TO HER THAT WAY!

WHAT'S **YOUR** PROBLEM? SHE'S JUST MY MOTHER...

IF **I** HAD A MOTHER, I'D TREAT HER BETTER. YOUR MOM DESERVES **RESPECT**!

HEY, LOOK AT THE DAUGHTER SHE PUTS UP WITH. SHE DESERVES AN **AWARD**.

HIGHNESS... HOW WOULD *YOU* FEEL IF CELIA WERE IN *MY* SITUATION? CAPTURED, HELD FAR AWAY FROM HOME? STUCK IN A ZOO SOMEWHERE?

WELL, I... *TERRIBLE,* I IMAGINE.

YEAH! SO JUST IMAGINE HOW KING TRITON'S GONNA FEEL WHEN HE FINDS OUT *HIS DAUGHTER* IS HERE--

KING TRITON! SO THIS IS A *PRINCESS* THEN! HER FATHER IS SOMEONE OF POWER!

OoOoooops!!

NICE *GOING,* FLOUNDER.

IF *THAT'S* THE CASE, THEN ALL I HAVE TO DO IS USE HIS DAUGHTER AS A BARGAINING CHIP... AND I COULD TAKE HIS ENTIRE KINGDOM!

CELIA, YOU HAVE DONE MORE *EXCELLENTLY* THAN I COULD HAVE *IMAGINED.*

THANK YOU, FATHER!

COME! LET'S *CELEBRATE!*

I'M *SORRY,* ARIEL.

I KNOW WHAT YOU MEAN, YOUR HIGHNESS. SO AM I.

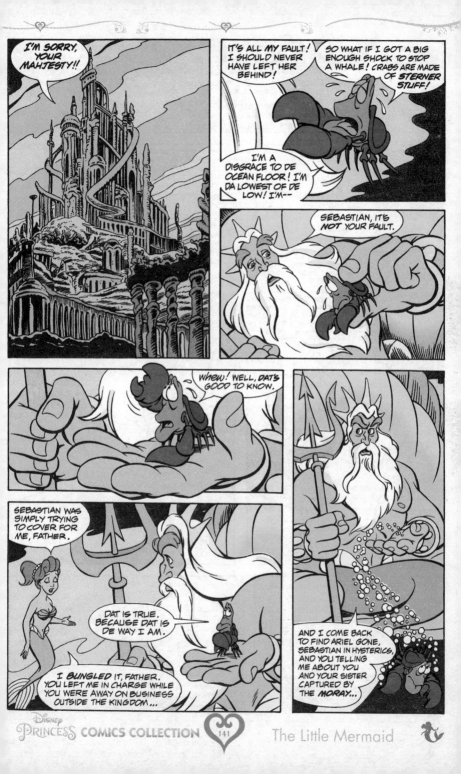

I'M SORRY, YOUR MAHJESTY!!

IT'S ALL MY FAULT! I SHOULD NEVER HAVE LEFT HER BEHIND!

SO WHAT IF I GOT A BIG ENOUGH SHOCK TO STOP A WHALE! CRABS ARE MADE OF STERNER STUFF!

I'M A DISGRACE TO DE OCEAN FLOOR! I'M DA LOWEST OF DE LOW! I'M--

SEBASTIAN, IT'S NOT YOUR FAULT.

WHEW! WELL, DAT'S GOOD TO KNOW.

SEBASTIAN WAS SIMPLY TRYING TO COVER FOR ME, FATHER.

DAT IS TRUE. BECAUSE DAT IS DE WAY I AM.

I BUNGLED IT, FATHER. YOU LEFT ME IN CHARGE WHILE YOU WERE AWAY ON BUSINESS OUTSIDE THE KINGDOM...

AND I COME BACK TO FIND ARIEL GONE, SEBASTIAN IN HYSTERICS, AND YOU TELLING ME ABOUT YOU AND YOUR SISTER CAPTURED BY THE MORAY...

THE MORAY? IS *THAT* THEIR NAME, FATHER? YOU KNOW WHO THEY ARE?

OF *COURSE* I DO, AQUATA. I'M THE KING OF THE SEA. I'M NOT EXACTLY UNINFORMED.

YOU RETURNED HERE AND LEFT ARIEL BEHIND, AQUATA. WHY DID YOU DO THAT?

--THEN PERHAPS NONE OF US WOULD HAVE THE CHANCE AGAIN. I THOUGHT BEING IN CHARGE MEANT DOING WHATEVER YOU *WANTED*. I NEVER REALIZED THAT, SOMETIMES, BEING IN CHARGE MEANS HAVING TO DO THINGS YOU'D MUCH RATHER *NOT* DO.

BECAUSE I DIDN'T HAVE ENOUGH RESOURCES TO HANDLE THINGS. AND IF I DIDN'T ESCAPE WHEN I HAD THE CHANCE--

I FAILED YOU, FATHER. I APOLOGIZE. AND I'D UNDERSTAND IF YOU NEVER LEFT ME IN CHARGE AGAIN.

FAILED ME? YOU TOOK RESPONSIBILITY, BLAMED NO ONE ELSE FOR THINGS THAT WENT WRONG, AND LEARNED A VALUABLE TRUTH OR TWO. *WHERE'S* THE FAILURE IN THAT?

THAT'S EXACTLY WHAT I'M GOING TO DO *AGAIN*, RIGHT NOW. I'LL RISK NONE OF MY PEOPLE, OR MORE OF MY DAUGHTERS, AGAINST THOSE SERPENTS.

AS FOR LEAVING YOU IN CHARGE...

I'LL ATTEND TO THE MORAY MYSELF.

DAT'S RIGHT. DE KING IS GOING TO SHOW DEM WHAT'S WHAT. OH, WHAT I'D GIVE TO SEE DAT...

I'M GLAD YOU FEEL THAT WAY, SEBASTIAN...

BECAUSE YOU'RE COMING ALONG.

EEEEP!

DEAD! WHAT DO YOU MEAN, THE SERPENTINE MONSTER IS DEAD?!

IT COULD NOT BE HELPED, YOUR HIGHNESS!

THE CREATURE WAS SO BERSERK FROM EVERYTHING THAT HAD HAPPENED--NOT TO MENTION BEING DEPRIVED OF HIS PREY--

THAT IT WAS IMPOSSIBLE FOR US TO TAKE HIM ALIVE. HE FOUGHT MUCH TOO FIERCELY IN HIS AGITATED STATE.

TO USE LESS THAN LETHAL FORCE AGAINST THE SERPENTINE WOULD HAVE MEANT THE LIVES OF MANY HUNTERS.

YES, YES. YOU'RE RIGHT, OF COURSE. BESIDES, I WOULDN'T WANT TO RISK LOSING ANY OF MY HUNTERS OR SOLDIERS NOW.

NOT WHEN I WILL NEED THEM IF WE GO TO WAR WITH THE MERPEOPLE.

WHAT SHALL WE DO WITH THE BODY OF THE SERPENTINE, HIGHNESS? WITH THE FESTIVAL ENDING PREMATURELY--

OH, I'LL BE MORE THAN HAPPY TO TAKE IT OFF YOUR HANDS.

BY THE DARK WATER--!

"LEARN SOMETHING FROM HER." LIKE *WHAT*? HOW TO BE A PRISONER?

LIKE HOW TO APPRECIATE YOUR MOTHER WHEN YOU HAVE ONE.

OH, AND I SUPPOSE YOU'RE ALWAYS PERFECT AND POLITE WHEN DEALING WITH YOUR ELDERS. WITH YOUR "KING TRITON."

OH, I WOULDN'T SAY *THAT*.

BUT EVEN WHEN I DISAGREE WITH HIM, I'M NOT RUDE WITH HIM THE WAY YOU ARE. I WAS BROUGHT UP *BETTER* THAN THAT.

I *SEE*. INSTEAD OF SAYING WHAT YOU THINK, YOU *ACT* RESPECTFUL AND THEN DO WHAT YOU WANT ANYWAY BEHIND HIS BACK.

YOU BET THAT'S WHAT SHE DOES! AND...

uhh...

...I'LL JUST WAIT OVER HERE AND STAY QUIET.

THANK YOU.

THERE'S SOME SORT OF COMMOTION IN THE MAIN SQUARE. I WONDER WHAT'S GOING **ON**!

THERE'S A **MOB** OUT THERE. AND THERE'S MY FATHER GOING OUT. SOMETHING BIG MUST BE HAPPENING.

IT MUST BE **DADDY**. WE'VE GOT TO GET OUT OF HERE, **QUICKLY**. MAYBE WE CAN HELP HIM.

OH, YEAH. THE SOONER WE FIND HIM, THE SOONER HE CAN CHEW US OUT FOR GETTING INTO THIS MESS.

Ahem.

ANNOUNCING DE ARRIVAL OF TRITON, DE KING OF DE SEVEN SEAS, DE FATHER OF DE MERMAID WHO YOU HAVE CAPTURED...

AND DE ONE WHO IS GOING TO GIVE YOU MORE **TROUBLE** DEN YOU COULD BELIEVE.

YOUR ANCESTOR, SINGLE-HANDEDLY, *DEFEATED* THE MORAY? AND CREATED THE LEGENDS OF HOW MERPEOPLE COULD BOIL OUR BLOOD? HAH!

THAT'S CORRECT.

MON, YOU DON'T KNOW WHO YOU'RE TALKING TO. DA SEA KING, HE COULD... WHY, HE COULD DE- STROY DAT BUILDING OVER DERE WIT *NO* PROBLEM AT ALL.

EVEN IF THAT *WERE* TRUE, I'D WAGER MY ANCESTOR DIDN'T HAVE A MERMAID PRINCESS AS *PRISONER!* HAND OVER THAT TRIDENT AND CROWN... OR HER LIFE IS FORFEIT.

NONSENSE! HE WOULDN'T *DARE!*

OH REALLY? *SHOW* HIM, YOUR MAJESTY.

FWZAAAAM

OOOOOFF!

HOW *DARE* YOU DO DAT TO THE SEA KING! WHY, JUST FOR DAT, HE'D PROBABLY BLOW DAT STATUE OF YOU OVER DERE TO *BITS!*

I'D LIKE TO SEE HIM *TRY!*

Panel 1:

STOP SINGING!! STOP IT!

HERE'S ONE YOU'LL LOVE. LISTEN...

YO HO YO HO, A PIRATE'S LIFE FOR ME...!

THANKS FOR WATCHING HER, SCUTTLE. I'LL TAKE IT FROM HERE.

Panel 2:

ALL RIGHT, "PRINCESS." YOU WON *THIS* ONE. BUT YOU CAN BET YOU HAVEN'T HEARD THE LAST OF THIS.

I WOULDN'T THROW AROUND THREATS IF *I* WERE YOU. REMEMBER... SCUTTLE KNOWS LOTS OF SONGS.

Panel 3:

WELL, SHE'S AN *OBNOXIOUS* YOUNG THING. AS FOR *YOU*, YOUNG LADY... I'M RELIEVED YOU'RE SAFE. HOWEVER...

OH, DADDY, I'M SO SORRY. YOU MADE A RULE, AND I IGNORED IT FOR NO GOOD REASON. BUT I'VE LEARNED FROM THIS. *REALLY.* AND FROM NOW ON, I'LL NEVER DISOBEY ANOTHER RULE...

Panel 4:

UNLESS IT'S FOR A GOOD REASON.

YES... I MEAN, NO! NO, I WOULDN'T EVER! NOT--

WE'LL DISCUSS IT FURTHER, ARIEL... AT HOME.

YES, DADDY.

Panel 5:

"YES, DADDY." THE GOOD LITTLE THING. HAAWWW HAW HAW!

I KNEW THAT FOOL CORNELIUS COULD *NEVER* CONQUER TRITON, AND EVEN IF HE'D *HAD*, EVEN IF HE'D OBTAINED THE TRIDENT AND CROWN AS I TOLD HIM TO, I'D STILL HAVE BEEN ABLE TO TRICK HIM OUT OF IT. BUT NO MATTER...

Panel 6:

...TRITON HAS HIS DAUGHTER, CORNELIUS HAS A CITY TO REBUILD, AND I...,

...THANKS TO THE BODY OF THE SERPENTINE MONSTER... HAVE A NEW HOME.

I SO *LOVE* A HAPPY ENDING.

HA HA HA HA

fin

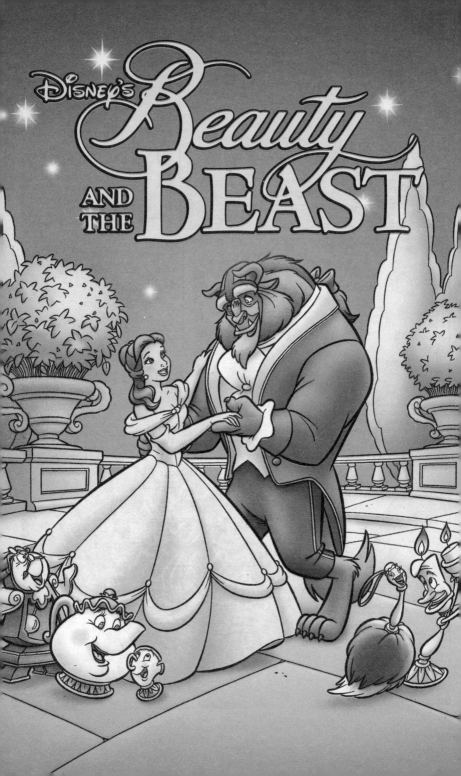

Panel 1:
WHAT'S HE SO *CRABBY* ABOUT, MAMA? WE'RE THE ONES WHO GOT TURNED INTO *FURNITURE* AND *DISHES*!

I RATHER THINK *WE* GOT THE *BEST* OF THE LOT, MY DEAR. I DON'T THINK *I* EVER LOOKED *BETTER*!

Panel 2:
WELL NO ONE ASKED *ME*! I WISH I'D BEEN TURNED INTO A *BIG FEROCIOUS BEAST*!

NOTHING HAS CHANGED...

Panel 3:
OUR LIVES ARE JUST THE SAME AS THEY ALWAYS WERE.

MAIS OUI! WE ARE TRULY *DEDICATED*!

I CERTAINLY HAVE *NOTHING BETTER TO DO* WITH MY TIME!

Panel 4:
I STILL SAY HE'S A *CRAB*!

I CAN'T SAY THE MASTER IS VERY MUCH CHANGED, EITHER.

OUI! THE *TANTRUMS* HE THREW AS A *CHILD* WERE *NO LESS* FIERCE!

MUST YOU TALK SO *LOUD*, LUMIERE?

Panel 5:
I *SPEAK MY MIND*, UNLIKE *YOU*, I *DO NOT HESITATE!*

I'LL HAVE YOU KNOW I HAVEN'T LOST A *SECOND* IN *ALL* THIS TIME!

Panel 6:
THE POOR SOUL WAS *ALWAYS* OFF ON THE *WRONG FOOT*.

THE MASTER MUST HAVE PULLED A *LULU* TO GET US INTO *THIS FIX*!

Panel 7:
IT'S *TRUE* HE WAS NOT THE *FRIENDLIEST* CHILD!

WOULDN'T GIVE A BEGGAR THE *TIME OF DAY*!

TELL ME *MORE* ABOUT THE *YOUNG PRINCE*, MAMA!

WELL...I'M NOT SPEAKING OF TIME AS COGSWORTH MARKS IT, BUT IT WAS LONG, LONG AGO...

NO ONE CAN TALK TO ME LIKE THAT!!!
Mon Dieu!
OH, DEAR! NO, NO!
IF YOU WANT YOUR PEOPLE'S LOVE, YOU MUST EARN THEIR RESPECT!
THEY WILL LOVE ME BECAUSE THEY HAVE TO!
I MUST APOLOGIZE FOR MY YOUNG--??
SHE IS GONE!!
NOT SURPRISING! SHE LOOKED LIKE A WITCH!
THE PRINCE GREW OLDER, BUT, ALAS, NOT WISER!
WE TRIED OUR BEST TO GUIDE HIM, BUT WHAT COULD WE DO?
OUR HANDS WERE TIED!
DID YOU SEE THAT, PAPA? DO ALL MEN HAVE TO BE MONSTERS?
I WISH YOU WOULDN'T MAKE SUCH GENERAL STATEMENTS, MY DEAR.

"There are forces which protect the weak and helpless. Alas, my charge was *neither.*"

BOY, IF HE REALLY WAS THAT MUCH OF A *JERK,* I THINK I LIKE HIM *BETTER NOW!*

(SIGH!) I AM NOT SO SURE I DO NOT *AGREE* WITH YOU.

HE NEVER LISTENED TO ME WHEN I TOLD HIM IT WAS BEDTIME. I'M SURE IF HE *HAD,* THINGS WOULD HAVE BEEN MUCH *BETTER.*

AND SO THE PRINCE TOOK HIS NAP, AND *WE ALL LIVED HAPPILY EVER AFTER!*

HE GOT MORE SLEEP THAN THE *REST* OF US, AS IT *WAS!*

NOW, NOW! IT WASN'T *EASY* TO SEE THE GOOD IN THE LAD, IT'S TRUE, BUT HE WAS AFTER ALL JUST A *BOY.*

He was an eager student and loved the books in the castle library."

"He had a surprisingly gentle way with you, Chip..."

"He needed someone to teach him a lesson. No denying that. If you aren't willing to change your own bad habits, someone else may come along and change them for you."

WE HAVEN'T SEEN THE END OF IT *YET.* MARK MY WORDS, THERE'S *STILL* MORE CHANGES TO COME.

KNOCK ON WOOD.

YOU'RE GETTING *WAX* ON ME!

WELL, I *STILL* DON'T SEE WHAT HE'S ALWAYS SO CRABBY ABOUT!

SHHHHH!

DO YOU WANT HIM TO *HEAR* YOU?

MRS. POTTS?

YES, MASTER?

I CAN'T FIND MUSIC BOX. HAVE YOU SEEN HIM?

I DO BELIEVE I HEARD HIM *SINGING* IN THE LIBRARY. YOU GO HAVE A LOOK, MASTER.

THERE'S YOUR ANSWER, CHIP. INSIDE THERE'S *STILL* A *LITTLE BOY* WHO HASN'T HAD HIS NAP.

HIS WRIGGLES OF EXCITEMENT TRIP *THIS LEVER* WHICH DROPS THE BAG OF SAND ONTO THIS *SPIKE*, WHICH SPLITS THE BAG AND SPILLS THE SAND INTO THIS *HOPPER*. IT POURS INTO THESE CUPS WHICH THEN TURNS THIS WHEEL CONNECTED TO THE MECHANISM WHICH DRIVES THESE POWERFUL DIGGING BLADES...

THE DIRT *PASSES THROUGH HERE* WHERE IT IS SIFTED THROUGH THIS MESH AND THE *TRUFFLES* ARE PLUCKED OUT AND DEPOSITED IN THIS *BUCKET*.

THEY MIGHT GET A BIT *MANGLED*, BUT THEN THEY GET CHOPPED UP ANYWAY.

ISN'T THAT A LOT OF *TROUBLE* FOR A *TRIFLING TRUFFLE?*

RICH PEOPLE PAY A *KING'S RANSOM* FOR THESE LITTLE TIDBITS, MY DEAR.

I KNOW ALL MY IDEAS HAVEN'T BEEN *PRAC-TICAL*, BELLE, BUT THIS TIME... ...OUR FORTUNE IS *ASSURED!*

NOW PUT THAT BOOK AWAY. THE DAY IS MUCH TOO FINE FOR YOU TO BE *IN HERE!*

I'M HAPPY WHERE I AM, PAPA!

NOW YOU GO FIND YOUR FRIENDS AND PLAY. WHEN YOU COME BACK, I'LL BE READY TO GIVE YOU A DEMONSTRATION!

BUT, PAPA, I DON'T...

...WANT TO GO OUT!

SLAM!

AVAST, YE LUBBERS! BELAY THE MIZZENS AND BATTEN THE POOP!

AAAARRRHHHH!

OOOOOOHHH!

TAKE THE WENCH PRISONER! WE NEED A GALLEY SLAVE!

WHAT YOU NEED IS A LONG WALK OFF A SHORT PLANK! I HAVE BETTER THINGS TO DO!

TAKE HER TO THE SHIP!

I WILL NOT PLAY YOUR SILLY PIRATE GAME!

PUT ME DOWN! IT'S NOT FUNNY!

TAKE ME PRISONER TOO!

AND ME!!

AND ME!!

Panel 1:
I DON'T KNOW WHAT'S IN THEM ANYMORE.

HAVE *YOU* ANY NOTIONS, COGSWORTH?

WELL... *ahem...* IF I MIGHT MAKE A RECOMMENDATION...

Panel 2:
I MYSELF HAVE *ahem!* HAD THE OCCASION TO UTILIZE THE WORDS OF THE POETS...

Panel 3:
THERE IS *NOTHING* KNOWN TO INTEREST A MAIDEN MORE THAN A *FLATTERING COMPARISON!*

I AM FOND OF SUCH A THING *MYSELF!*

Panel 4:
YOU WANT *ME* TO...??!

SPEAK IT AS THOUGH IT IS QUINTESSENTIALLY YOUR EXPRESS INTENTION!

SAY WHAT YOU MEAN, COGSWORTH!

Panel 5:
I THOUGHT I MADE MYSELF CLEAR!

WE ARE SPEAKING OF AMOUR, NOT TIMETABLES!

SILENCE!!

Panel 6:
HOW CAN I SPEAK OF *LOVE* WITH YOUR INCESSANT BABBLE ABOUT *ROMANCE??!!*

I believe that
true beauty
is found within.

I am a Princess

Belle

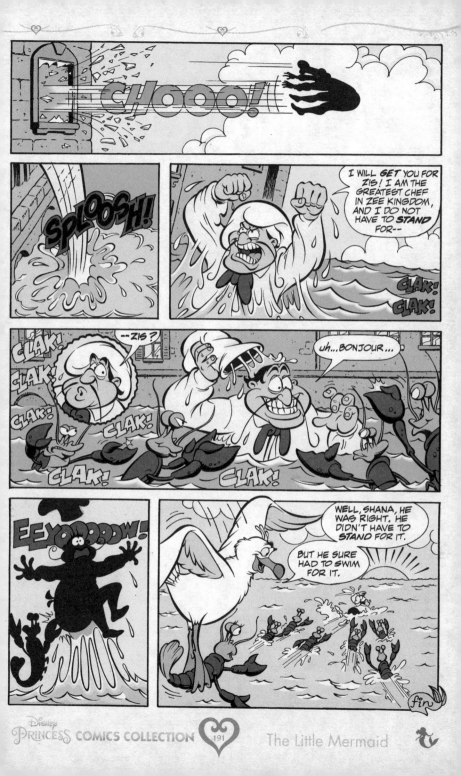

Cinderella

Cinderella

ONCE UPON A TIME, IN A FARAWAY LAND, THERE WAS A GENTLEMAN WHO LIVED IN A STATELY HOUSE WITH HIS LITTLE DAUGHTER.

ONE DAY, FEELING THAT SHE NEEDED A MOTHER, HE DECIDED TO MARRY AGAIN.

HE CHOSE FOR HIS WIFE A WOMAN WITH TWO DAUGHTERS OF HER OWN.

WHEN THE GENTLEMAN DIED, THE STEPMOTHER BEHAVED CRUELLY TO HER STEPDAUGHTER.

THE CHILD, WHO WAS MADE A SERVANT IN HER OWN HOUSE, GREW INTO A BEAUTIFUL YOUNG GIRL. SHE USED TO WARM HER FEET IN THE CINDERS NEAR THE CHIMNEY, SO PEOPLE CALLED HER CINDERELLA...

=TRRR TWEET TWEET!=

=CHEEPCHEEP-CHEEP!=

OH! YOU WOKE ME UP RIGHT IN THE MIDDLE OF A LOVELY DREAM!

YES, I KNOW, IT'S BEAUTIFUL WEATHER!

BUT MY DREAM WAS BEAUTIFUL, TOO!

BOTHER THAT CLOCK! SPOIL-SPORT! "GET UP, CINDERELLA, TIME TO GO TO WORK!" EVEN THE CLOCK GIVES ME ORDERS!

BUT NO ONE CAN STOP ME FROM DREAMING!

ONE DAY MY DREAM WILL COME TRUE...

CINDERELLA! CINDERELLA! HURRY! HURRY!

I'LL TELL HER! I'LL TELL HER!

NO! I'LL TELL HER!

DON'T BOTH TALK AT ONCE! ONE AT A TIME! WHAT'S GOING ON?

THERE'S A *MOUSE* IN THE HOUSE! CAN YOU IMAGINE THAT?!

A *MOUSE*? WHY, WE'LL TAKE CARE OF IT. FIRST, LET'S FIND IT A DRESS...

A *DRESS*? NO, NO, IT ISN'T A GIRL, IT'S A *BOY*!

IT'S IN A TRAP!

IN A *TRAP*? WE MUST GO AND *RELEASE* IT, QUICKLY!

SOON...

OH! POOR THING, IT'S *FRIGHTENED* TO DEATH.

ZUK! ZUK! DON'T BE SCARED. CINDERELLA'S A *FRIEND*, SHE'S VERY *KIND*!

HERE'S A SWEATER...IT'S A LITTLE SNUG, BUT IT'LL HAVE TO DO FOR NOW! I CHRISTEN YOU OCTAVIUS, *GUS* FOR SHORT.

NOW I MUST GET TO WORK. LOOK AFTER HIM, *JAQ*, AND DON'T FORGET TO *WARN* HIM ABOUT THE *CAT*!

HAVE YOU EVER *SEEN* THE CAT? HE *BITES*, HE *CLAWS*, HE'S *SLY*! HE'S FAT! FAT! *FAT*! ZUK ZUK *LUCIFER*!

GRRR! WOOF! *WOOF!*

WAKE UP, BRUNO! YOU WERE CHASING LUCIFER IN YOUR SLEEP AGAIN!

AND *THIS* TIME, YOU'D FINALLY *CAUGHT* HIM!

LISTEN--IF YOU WANT TO KEEP THAT BONE, DREAM OF SOMETHING ELSE... *LEARN TO LIKE CATS!*

YES, I KNOW, IT'S NOT EASY.

LUCIFER CAN BE BAD AT TIMES, BUT...

...SURELY HE ISN'T *JUST* A BIG MEANIE!

ZUK! ZUK! *BREAKFAST!*

HEY! NO, WAIT!

TOO DANGEROUS. LUCIFER! REMEMBER LUCIFER!

LET'S SEE...WHAT SHALL WE DO?

I KNOW! ONE OF US WILL CATCH LUCIFER'S ATTENTION!

LET'S PICK A TAIL TO SEE WHO'LL CARRY OUT THIS MISSION!

SO?

UH...LOOKS LIKE IT'S ME!

~GULP!~

BRAVO! BRAVO! BRAVO!

SUDDENLY...

DING!
DING!
DING!

COMING, COMING!

YES, YES! JUST A MINUTE!

DING! DING!

CINDERELLA! CINDERELLA!

IT'S BREAKFAST TIME FOR CINDERELLA'S STEPMOTHER AND HER TWO DAUGHTERS, AND THAT MEANS EVEN MORE WORK...

MORNING TO EVENING... ORDERS! ALWAYS ORDERS!

GOOD MORNING, DRIZELLA! DID YOU SLEEP WELL?

IT'S NONE OF YOUR BUSINESS!

Cinderella

WHY SHOULDN'T YOU GO? IF YOU FINISH ALL YOUR CHORES... AND IF YOU HAVE A SUITABLE DRESS TO WEAR!

THANK YOU, MOTHER!

MOTHER! DO YOU REALIZE WHAT YOU'VE SAID?

YES, OF COURSE...

...I SAID, "IF."

OH! SO YOU DID!

HEE HEE HEE!

CINDERELLA IS TOO HAPPY TO REALIZE HER STEPMOTHER HAS TRICKED HER.

LOOK AT THIS LOVELY DRESS! IT BELONGED TO MY MOTHER!

IT'S A BIT OLD-FASHIONED, BUT I CAN ALTER IT.

I COULD COPY ONE OF THESE DESIGNS!

VERY PRETTY! ~SQUEAK! SQUEAK!~

I LOVE IT! ZUK! ZUK!

I'LL SHORTEN THE SLEEVES, ADD A BELT, PUT LACE ROUND THE NECK, ADD A BIG RIBBON AND...

CINDERELLA! CINDERELLA! CINDERELLA!

OH, NO. WHAT DO THEY WANT *NOW*?

TOO BAD! THE DRESS WILL JUST HAVE TO WAIT.

AS SOON AS CINDERELLA STOPS FOR A MINUTE, THOSE TWO START SHRIEKING AT HER!

YOU KNOW WHAT? CINDERELLA WON'T GO TO THE BALL!

WHAT? YOU'RE KIDDING!

WHAT ARE YOU TALKING ABOUT?

YOU'LL SEE, THEY'LL STOP HER! THEY'LL MAKE HER WORK ALL DAY AND THE DRESS WILL *NEVER* BE READY!

THEN WE'LL HELP HER! IT ISN'T HARD TO ALTER A DRESS. WHEN YOU HAVE THE KNACK, IT'S A PIECE OF CAKE!

WE JUST NEED LACE, RIBBONS, AND PEARL GO ON, HURRY!

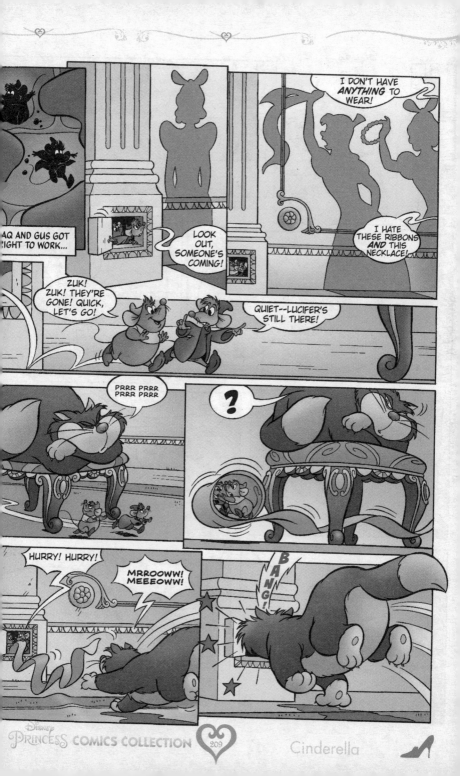

Disney
PRINCESS COMICS COLLECTION

Cinderella

OOOH!

SURPRISE! SURPRISE! SQUEEK! SQUEEK!

HAPPY BIRTHDAY!

BE QUIET SILLY!

OH, I'M SO HAPPY! HOW *KIND* OF YOU. THANK YOU, WITH *ALL* MY HEART!

NOW, DON'T FORGET, WHEN YOU'RE INTRODUCED TO THE PRINCE--

WAIT!

PLEASE, WAIT FOR ME!

CINDERELLA!

DISNEY PRINCESS COMICS COLLECTION

Cinderella

FOR SUCH AN ELEGANT CARRIAGE, WE NEED... MICE!

MICE?

HA! SWEET LITTLE THINGS. PERFECT!

ABRACADABRA! HEY, PRESTO!

NOW, FOR THE HORSE. AS A COACHMAN, FAITHFUL STEED, TO THE BALL YOUR MISTRESS LEAD!

AND THE DOG! BRUNO, FOR JUST ONE NIGHT, BE A FOOTMAN DRESSED IN WHITE!

EXCUSE ME, BUT DON'T YOU THINK MY DRESS...

OH! GOOD HEAVENS, MY DEAR, JUST LOOK AT THOSE RAGS!

WHAT WAS I THINKING OF? ABRACADABRA! HEY, PRESTO!

NOW, CINDERELLA, REMEMBER--ON THE LAST STROKE OF MIDNIGHT, THE SPELL WILL BE BROKEN AND EVERYTHING WILL BE AS BEFORE. HURRY! THE BALL IS WAITING AND TIME WILL FLY!

THE CARRIAGE SPED TOWARDS THE ROYAL PALACE...

AT THE PALACE, THE YOUNG GIRLS INVITED TO THE BALL WERE BEING PRESENTED TO THE PRINCE...

PRINCESS FREDERIKA-EUGENIA DE LA FONTAINE!

~HUMPH!~ YOU CAN'T SAY HE'S BEING VERY COOPERATIVE!

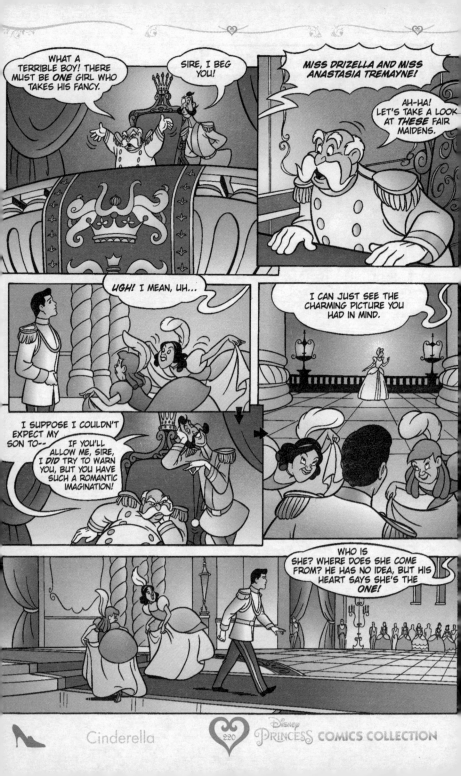

WHAT A TERRIBLE BOY! THERE MUST BE ONE GIRL WHO TAKES HIS FANCY.

SIRE, I BEG YOU!

MISS DRIZELLA AND MISS ANASTASIA TREMAYNE!

AH-HA! LET'S TAKE A LOOK AT THESE FAIR MAIDENS.

UGH! I MEAN, UH...

I CAN JUST SEE THE CHARMING PICTURE YOU HAD IN MIND.

I SUPPOSE I COULDN'T EXPECT MY SON TO--

IF YOU'LL ALLOW ME, SIRE, I DID TRY TO WARN YOU, BUT YOU HAVE SUCH A ROMANTIC IMAGINATION!

WHO IS SHE? WHERE DOES SHE COME FROM? HE HAS NO IDEA, BUT HIS HEART SAYS SHE'S THE ONE!

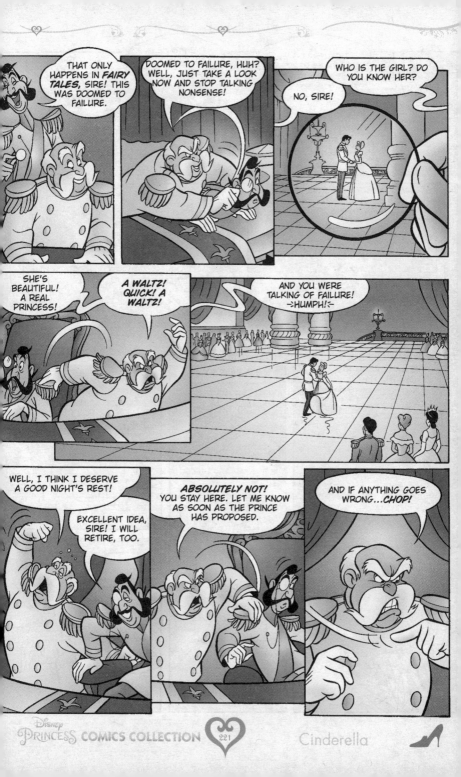

DONG!

DONG!

DONG!

MY DEAR FRIENDS! I FORGOT EVERYTHING TONIGHT, EVEN THE TIME! BUT IT WAS SO WONDERFUL! HE WAS SO HANDSOME, SO CHARMING, SO GALLANT. OH, WELL, IT'S OVER NOW!

LOOK, CINDERELLA! THE SLIPPER!

OH, THANK YOU! THANK YOU FOR EVERYTHING, DEAR GODMOTHER!

Cinderella

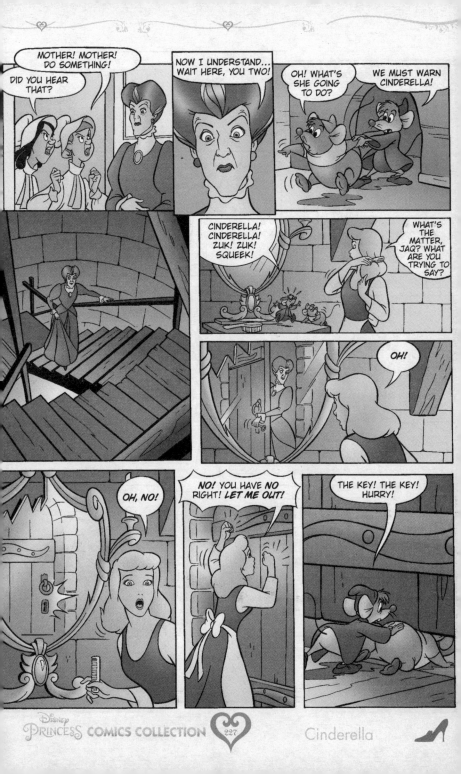

...THE AIM OF THE INQUIRY BEING THAT EVERY MAIDEN IN OUR BELOVED KINGDOM TRY THE SLIPPER ON FOR SIZE...

...AND IF THE SLIPPER FITS...

...THE MAIDEN WILL BE THE ONE AND ONLY BRIDE OF HIS ROYAL HIGHNESS, OUR NOBLE PRINCE.

...THE PRESENT ROYAL DECREE WILL BE READ EACH DWELLING IN THE KING'S NAME.

LET US PROCEED ~YAWN~ TO THE FITTING!

THERE. I *SAID* IT WAS MY SLIPPER!

UMM, OF COURSE IT'S JUST A LITTLE TIGHT TODAY. MY FEET ARE SWOLLEN AFTER DANCING ALL NIGHT.

HURRY, GUS! LET'S TAKE IT TO CINDERELLA!

COME ON, GUS, WE'RE NEARLY THERE!

JUST ONE MORE LITTLE EFFORT!

-HUF- -HUFFF-

IT'S UP THERE!

MEANWHILE, IN THE DRAWING ROOM, THE FITTING CONTINUES...

YOU CLUMSY DOLT! YOU'RE NOT REALLY TRYING! I HAVE A GOOD MIND TO SLAP YOU!

OOOOOH!

THAT WILL DO! NEXT YOUNG GIRL!

YUK! YUK! WE'RE COMING!

IS THAT YOU? YOU'VE GOT THE KEY!

MEEEOOOWW!

WHAM

OH, **NO!** NO NO **NO!** I'M A **GONER!** THE KING WILL HAVE MY **HEAD!**

YOUR GRACE, I'VE GOT THE **OTHER** SLIPPER!

IT FITS YOU **PERFECTLY**, YOUNG LADY!

HOORAY FOR CINDERELLA! **HOORAY!**

Cinderella

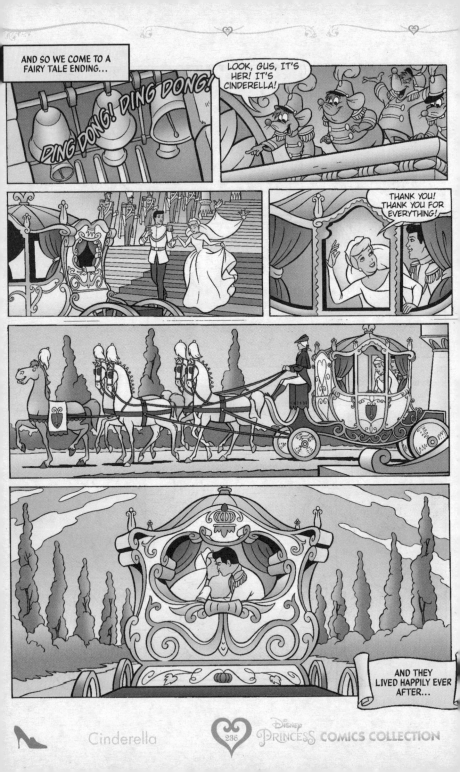

I believe that
love binds us together,
kindness is power
and dreams really
do come true.

I am a Princess

Cinderella

I am a princess.

I'm brave sometimes.
I'm scared sometimes.
Sometimes, I'm brave even when I'm scared.

I believe in loyalty.
And trust.
I believe loyalty is built on trust.